Volume Ten

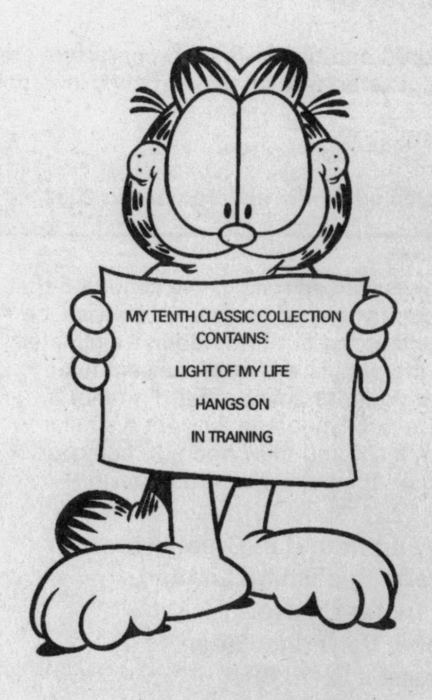

JIM DAVIS

RR

© 2002 PAWS, INCORPORATED
All rights reserved.

"GARFIELD" and the GARFIELD characters are registered and unregistered trademarks of Paws, Incorporated.

(www.garfield.com)

First published by Ravette Publishing 2002

This book is sold subject to the condition that it shall not, by way of trade or otherwise, be lent, resold, hired out or otherwise circulated without the publisher's prior consent in any form of binding or cover other than that in which it is published and without a similar condition including this condition being imposed on the subsequent purchaser.

Printed and bound in Great Britain
for Ravette Publishing Limited,
Unit 3, Tristar Centre,
Star Road, Partridge Green,
West Sussex RH13 8RA

by Cox & Wyman Ltd, Reading, Berkshire

ISBN: 1 84161 150 6

Garfield

Light Of My Life

JIM DAVIS

RR

© 1992 United Feature Syndicate, Inc.

I'LL HAVE THE SPAGHETTI, IRMA
JIM DAVIS 3-20

DO YOU WANT THAT ON A PLATE?
OF COURSE I DO!
© 1992 United Feature Syndicate, Inc.

WELL EXCUSE ME, MISTER PICKY!
IS IT TOO MUCH TO BE ACCORDED THE SAME AMENITIES OTHERS GET?! I'M A PERSON TOO, YOU KNOW!!
I'LL JUST HAVE A SMALL SLICE OF LIFE, THANK YOU

© 1992 United Feature Syndicate, Inc.

© 1992 United Feature Syndicate, Inc.

© 1992 United Feature Syndicate, Inc.

© 1992 United Feature Syndicate, Inc.

WHAT HAPPENED HERE, GARFIELD?!

3-26
JIM DAVIS
YOU WOULDN'T UNDERSTAND
© 1992 United Feature Syndicate, Inc.

YOU'VE DESTROYED THE HOUSE!
YOU FIGURED IT OUT!

© 1992 United Feature Syndicate, Inc.

I'M NOT TYING JON'S SHOELACES TOGETHER ANYMORE

IT'S TOO DULL
© 1992 United Feature Syndicate, Inc.
JIM DAVIS 3-28

MISTER FUNNY MAN!
I'M FORGING NEW FRONTIERS

© 1992 United Feature Syndicate, Inc.

THE NIGHT STALKER CLOSES IN ON HIS PREY

SNAP
JIM DAVIS 3-31
© 1992 United Feature Syndicate, Inc.

AND SPENDS THE REST OF THE EVENING WITH HIS LIPS IN A MOUSETRAP

© 1992 United Feature Syndicate, Inc.

WELL, IT TOOK
A LOT OF WORK

BUT IT'S
WORTH IT
© 1992 United Feature Syndicate, Inc.

GARFIELD'S
"BIRDBATH OF DEATH"
JIM DAVIS 4-2

© 1992 United Feature Syndicate, Inc.

I WONDER IF JON WILL BE ABLE TO FIX MY ALARM CLOCK?..
© 1992 United Feature Syndicate, Inc.
JIM DAVIS 4-4

ONCE I'VE BROKEN IT

NEW NEIGHBORS, GARFIELD

DOESN'T LOOK GOOD
JIM DAVIS 4-6
© 1992 United Feature Syndicate, Inc.

IF THE YAK GETS OFF THE LEASH, I'M OUTTA HERE

JIM DAVIS 4-7
BEWARE OF THE DOG

WANT TO SEE SLIDES OF MY VACATION?
BEWARE OF THE DOG
© 1992 United Feature Syndicate, Inc.

YAAAAAHHHH!!!
BEWARE OF THE

© 1992 United Feature Syndicate, Inc.

JPM DAVPS 4-9
© 1992 United Feature Syndicate, Inc.

I DIDN'T KNOW YOU COULD WHISTLE!
I ATE A CANARY

© 1992 United Feature Syndicate, Inc.

© 1992 United Feature Syndicate, Inc.

© 1992 United Feature Syndicate, Inc.

© 1992 United Feature Syndicate, Inc.

Z
JIM DAVIS 4-14

YAWN

YAWN
© 1982 United Feature Syndicate, Inc.

YAWNED TOO BIG
JIM DAVIS 4-15

JIM DAVIS 4-16

I LOVE HELPING JON CLEAN THE REFRIGERATOR...
© 1992 United Feature Syndicate, Inc.

WE MAKE SANDWICHES OUT OF EVERYTHING!
NOW IF I SPREAD PEANUT BUTTER ON THE PICKLES, THE PEAS WON'T ROLL OFF...

© 1992 United Feature Syndicate, Inc.

© 1992 United Feature Syndicate, Inc.

© 1992 United Feature Syndicate, Inc.

TIME TO FEED GARFIELD!
GARFIE

TIME TO EAT!
© 1992 United Feature Syndicate, Inc.

YOU'RE LATE AGAIN!
I GOTTA WORK ON MY TIMING
GARFIE
JIM DAVIS 4-21

© 1992 United Feature Syndicate, Inc.

© 1992 United Feature Syndicate, Inc.

© 1992 United Feature Syndicate, Inc.

© 1992 United Feature Syndicate, Inc.

WE'VE RUN OUT OF SHOWS!

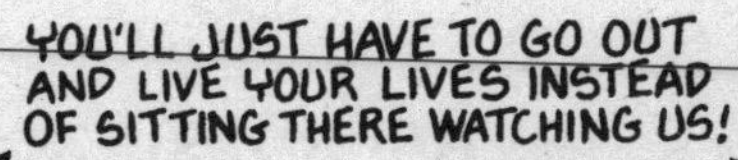
YOU'LL JUST HAVE TO GO OUT AND LIVE YOUR LIVES INSTEAD OF SITTING THERE WATCHING US!

© 1992 United Feature Syndicate, Inc.

JUST KIDDING!
WHEW!
JIM DAVIS 4-27

© 1992 United Feature Syndicate, Inc.

© 1992 United Feature Syndicate, Inc.

© 1992 United Feature Syndicate, Inc

JIM DAVIS 5-1

WELL, I'M HERE TO DO SOME OF THAT ADORABLE "CAT STUFF"
© 1992 United Feature Syndicate, Inc.

LET ME KNOW WHEN IT'S TIME FOR MY BREAK

© 1992 United Feature Syndicate, Inc.

© 1992 United Feature Syndicate, Inc.

© 1992 United Feature Syndicate, Inc.

© 1992 United Feature Syndicate, Inc.

WE HAVE A VERY SPECIAL GUEST TODAY

THE INVENTOR OF THE REMOTE CONTROL!
© 1992 United Feature Syndicate, Inc.

JIM DAVIS 5-7
CLICK

© 1992 United Feature Syndicate, Inc.

© 1992 United Feature Syndicate, Inc.

© 1992 United Feature Syndicate, Inc.

© 1992 United Feature Syndicate, Inc.

© 1992 United Feature Syndicate, Inc.

© 1992 United Feature Syndicate, Inc.

© 1992 United Feature Syndicate, Inc.

DEEP DOWN INSIDE, THE DOMESTIC CAT REMAINS A PRIMAL BEAST

IF YOU ARE WISE, YOU WILL FEAR ME
© 1992 United Feature Syndicate, Inc.

IF YOU WANT ME, I'LL BE PLAYING WITH MY TEDDY BEAR
JIM DAVIS 5-16

GOOD MORNING, JON

GOOD MORNING, GARF-
YAAAAAHHHHH!!!
© 1992 United Feature Syndicate, Inc.

TAKE OUT MY CONTACT LENSES!!
JIM DAVIS 5-18

HERE, GARFIELD. THIS IS A NEW KIND OF CAT FOOD
GARFIELD

GULP!
GARFI
© 1992 United Feature Syndicate, Inc.
JIM DAVIS 5-19

FUNNY... IT DOESN'T **SOUND** ANY DIFFERENT
GARFIELD

ON LONG ROAD TRIPS SOME PEOPLE LIKE TO READ, SOME PEOPLE LIKE TO SING...

BUMP BUMP BUMP
© 1992 United Feature Syndicate, Inc.

I LIKE TO LOOSEN LUG NUTS
JIM DAVIS 5-20

I TOLD YOU, GARFIELD. YOU CAN'T COME IN WITH ME! NOW WAIT THERE!
ED'S MARKET
JIM DAVIS 5-21

MR. ARBUCKLE, IS THAT YOUR CAR ALARM?
NO
HONK
HONK
HONK
HONK
ED'S
© 1992 United Feature Syndicate, Inc.

AND LAY OFF THE HORN!!!
ED'S
HONK
HONK

JON, I ACCIDENTALLY DROPPED YOUR GREAT-GREAT-GRANDMOTHER'S GRAVY BOAT

I'M SORRY
© 1992 United Feature Syndicate, Inc.
© JIM DAVIS 5-22

YOU NEVER LIKED THIS GRAVY BOAT, DID YOU?
HAD TO ACCIDENTALLY DROP THE SUCKER 47 TIMES

BANZAI!
JIM DAVIS 5-23

SPLASH
© 1992 United Feature Syndicate, Inc.

WHY DIDN'T YOU WARN ME WE WERE HAVING SOUP?

© 1992 United Feature Syndicate, Inc.

© 1992 United Feature Syndicate, Inc.

© 1992 United Feature Syndicate, Inc.

© 1992 United Feature Syndicate, Inc.

© 1992 United Feature Syndicate, Inc.

© 1992 United Feature Syndicate, Inc.

© 1992 United Feature Syndicate, Inc.

© 1992 United Feature Syndicate, Inc.

© 1992 United Feature Syndicate, Inc.

© 1992 United Feature Syndicate, Inc.

© 1992 United Feature Syndicate, Inc

© 1992 United Feature Syndicate, Inc.

© 1992 United Feature Syndicate, Inc.

HELLO THERE, MR. LAZY

STICKS AND STONES MAY BREAK MY BONES, BUT WORDS WILL NEVER HURT ME
© 1992 United Feature Syndicate, Inc.

HOG DANDRUFF!
MY LAWYERS, HOWEVER, FEEL OTHERWISE
JIM DAVIS 6-9

© 1992 United Feature Syndicate, Inc.

© 1992 United Feature Syndicate, Inc.

© 1992 United Feature Syndicate, Inc.

© 1992 United Feature Syndicate, Inc.

© 1992 United Feature Syndicate, Inc.

© 1992 United Feature Syndicate, Inc.

© 1992 United Feature Syndicate, Inc.

© 1992 United Feature Syndicate, Inc.

© 1992 United Feature Syndicate. Inc.

© 1992 United Feature Syndicate, Inc.

© 1992 United Feature Syndicate, Inc.

© 1992 United Feature Syndicate, Inc.

BOREDOM INSPECTOR!

HMMMM
© 1992 United Feature Syndicate, Inc.

JIM DAVIS 6-24
KEEP UP THE GOOD WORK
PAT
PAT

© 1992 United Feature Syndicate, Inc.

© 1992 United Feature Syndicate, Inc.

WATCH HOW JON'S FACE LIGHTS UP WHEN I ENTER THE ROOM

JIM DAVIS 6-27
© 1982 United Feature Syndicate, Inc.

OKAY, MAYBE "LIGHTS UP" WAS A POOR CHOICE OF WORDS

© 1992 United Feature Syndicate, Inc.

GARFIELD, FETCH MY SLIPPERS

SORRY, CATS DON'T FETCH SLIPPERS
© 1992 United Feature Syndicate, Inc.
JIM DAVIS 6-30

I WILL HOWEVER, FETCH THE FETCHER

© 1992 United Feature Syndicate, Inc.

DID YOU KNOW CATS CAN TALK? WE JUST DON'T CHOOSE TO

GARFIELD, I'M HOME!
WHO CARES?!
© 1992 United Feature Syndicate, Inc.

IF WE DID, **NOBODY** WOULD LIKE US
JIM DAVIS 7-2

© 1992 United Feature Syndicate, Inc.

© 1992 United Feature Syndicate, Inc.

© 1992 United Feature Syndicate, Inc.

© 1992 United Feature Syndicate, Inc.

© 1992 United Feature Syndicate, Inc.

© 1992 United Feature Syndicate, Inc.

© 1992 United Feature Syndicate, Inc.

© 1992 United Feature Syndicate, Inc.

© 1992 United Feature Syndicate, Inc.

© 1992 United Feature Syndicate, Inc.

© 1992 United Feature Syndicate, Inc.

© 1992 United Feature Syndicate, Inc.

© 1992 United Feature Syndicate, Inc.

© 1992 United Feature Syndicate, Inc.

© 1992 United Feature Syndicate, Inc.

© 1992 United Feature Syndicate, Inc.

© 1992 United Feature Syndicate, Inc.

JIM DAVIS 7-23
COOKIE CRUMB!

BANZAI!
© 1992 United Feature Syndicate, Inc.

COME TO PAPA!
DIET GETTING TO YOU, GARFIELD?

I'M PROUD TO REPORT I'VE GAINED ONLY ONE POUND!

© 1992 United Feature Syndicate, Inc.

WITH GARFIELD, THE GOAL OF A DIET ISN'T LOSING WEIGHT, IT'S SLOWING DOWN THE GAIN
JIM DAVIS 7-24

© 1992 United Feature Syndicate, Inc.

© 1992 United Feature Syndicate, Inc.

AH, NATURE!
JIM DAVIS 7-28

© 1992 United Feature Syndicate, Inc.

NEEDS VACUUMING

© 1992 United Feature Syndicate, Inc.

© 1992 United Feature Syndicate, Inc.

GIANT SCORPIONS!

THE WOLFMAN IS HEADED THIS WAY!
JIM DAVIS 7-31
© 1992 United Feature Syndicate, Inc.

KING KONG HAS A HEAD COLD AND WANTS TO BORROW YOUR HANDKERCHIEF!
I'M NOT MOVING TILL I FINISH THIS SANDWICH

© 1992 United Feature Syndicate, Inc.

I HATE BIRDS
JIM DAVIS 8-1

SO, DOCTOR, ARE DOGS MORE INTELLIGENT THAN CATS?

WELL, DOGS SCORED VERY HIGH IN TESTING
...AND CATS?
© 1992 United Feature Syndicate, Inc.

WELL, THEY WOULDN'T TAKE THE TEST
WE HAVE NOTHING TO PROVE
JIM DAVIS
8-3

© 1992 United Feature Syndicate, Inc.

© 1992 United Feature Syndicate, Inc.

© 1992 United Feature Syndicate, Inc.

© 1992 United Feature Syndicate, Inc.

WELL, GARFIELD, FOR DINNER YOU ATE ALL THE FOOD IN THE HOUSE
JIM DAVIS 8-8

THAT'S POOR PLANNING!
NO IT'S NOT
© 1992 United Feature Syndicate, Inc.

WHAT ARE YOU GOING TO DO IN THE MORNING, HUH?
I PLAN TO SLEEP THROUGH BREAKFAST

Garfield
Hangs On

JIM DAVIS

RR

PEOPLE WHO HAVE SIMPLE PLEASURES SHOULD BE ADMIRED

FUZZY BUNNY SLIPPERS!... CUTE BUNNY SLIPPERS!... COMFY BUNNY SLIPPERS!
© 1992 United Feature Syndicate, Inc.

...AND THEN EXECUTED
JIM DAVIS 8-10

SOUP?

© 1992 United Feature Syndicate, Inc.

IS THIS A HINT?
YOU'RE GETTING DANGEROUSLY CLOSE TO LUNCH TIME
JIM DAVIS 8-11

YOU ARE WATCHING THE NATIONAL DOG CHANNEL

AND NOW THE HEADLINES...
© 1992 United Feature Syndicate, Inc.

CATS SPREAD DISEASE!
I HATE BIASED REPORTING
JIM DAVIS 8-12

WATCH IT, CAT! I HAVE FIDO WITH ME TODAY!

WELL, BRING ON THIS FIDO
HEERE, FIDO!
© 1992 United Feature Syndicate, Inc.

MAIL'S HERE
JIM DAVIS 8-13

WELL, IT'S FRIDAY NIGHT
JIM DAVIS 8-14

OOOH! AAHHH! WOO! WOO! OOOOHH!
© 1992 United Feature Syndicate, Inc.

THERE IT IS!
TIME FOR A ROUSING GAME OF "FIND THE ICE CUBE"

© 1992 United Feature Syndicate, Inc.

JIM DAVIS 8-17
LADIES AND GENTLEMEN... MR. EXCITEMENT!

I RECKON IT MIGHT RAIN... UNLESS THE SUN COMES OUT, OF COURSE
© 1992 United Feature Syndicate, Inc.

GO BACK TO YOUR HOMES! MR. EXCITEMENT HAS SPOKEN!

© 1992 United Feature Syndicate, Inc.

© 1992 United Feature Syndicate, Inc.

© 1992 United Feature Syndicate, Inc.

JIM DAVIS 8·21
GARFIELD

© 1992 United Feature Syndicate, Inc.

THIS TASTES FUNNY
IF YOU ADD WATER, IT MAKES ITS OWN GRAVY

© 1992 United Feature Syndicate, Inc.

© 1992 United Feature Syndicate, Inc.

© 1992 United Feature Syndicate, Inc.

© 1992 United Feature Syndicate, Inc.

© 1992 United Feature Syndicate, Inc.

JIM DAVIS 8-28

YOU'RE STANDING ON MY FOOT!!
© 1992 United Feature Syndicate, Inc.

MY, WE'RE RATHER SELF-ABSORBED TODAY, AREN'T WE?

I'M WATCHING TELEVISION WITH A CAT
JIM DAVIS
8-29

I'M WATCHING TELEVISION WITH A CAT!
IT'S SATURDAY NIGHT
© 1992 United Feature Syndicate, Inc.

I'M WATCHING TELEVISION WITH A CAT!!
AND REALITY REARS ITS UGLY HEAD

© 1992 United Feature Syndicate, Inc.

© 1992 United Feature Syndicate, Inc.

© 1992 United Feature Syndicate, Inc.

DID YOU BRING YOUR WIFE TO THE REUNION, ARBUCKLE?
NOPE
THOM
JON
JIM DAVIS 9-13

GIRLFRIEND?
ACTUALLY, I BROUGHT MY CAT
THOM
JON
© 1992 United Feature Syndicate, Inc.

HEY, ARBUCKLE BROUGHT A CAT!
I SENSE HOSTILITY
JON

© 1992 United Feature Syndicate, Inc.

© 1992 United Feature Syndicate, Inc.

YES, JENNIFER, SINCE HIGH SCHOOL I'VE BECOME SOMEWHAT OF A SOPHISTICATE
JIM DAVIS 9-7
JON

I'VE MATURED IN-
HEY, CARPFACE!
JON
© 1992 United Feature Syndicate, Inc.

REMEMBER THE TIME YOU BLEW YOUR NOSE ON THE SCHOOL FLAG?
LATER, WHEEZER

HEY, CARPFACE, SURE IS A GREAT CLASS REUNION, HUH?
SURE IS, WHEEZER
JON

REMEMBER THE TIME I THREW YOUR PANTS INTO THE GIRLS' LOCKER ROOM?
YEAH, YOU WERE YOUNG AND CRAZY THEN
JON
© 1992 United Feature Syndicate, Inc.

NOW YOU'RE JUST CRAZY!
I LOVE NOSTALGIA
JIM DAVIS 9-8

ELMO! AFTER ALL THESE YEARS! GOOD TO SEE YOU!
MY NAME'S NOT ELMO
JIM DAVIS

OH, OF COURSE... GEORGE!
NOPE
ED!
NOPE
FRANK!
NOPE. IT'S JON
9-9
© 1992 United Feature Syndicate, Inc.

RIIIGHT! JON! WHY, YOU HAVEN'T CHANGED A BIT!
WHO THE HECK ARE YOU?

MRS. FRONZAK, MY OLD ENGLISH TEACHER!

WHAT ARE YOU DOING AT THE CLASS REUNION?
WAITING ON THAT OVERDUE TERM PAPER, JONNY
JIM DAVIS 9-10
© 1992 United Feature Syndicate, Inc.

MY, UH, CAT ATE IT!
LEAVE ME OUT OF THIS!

MRS. FRONZAK, I DIDN'T KNOW TEACHERS WERE INVITED TO THE CLASS REUNION
I'M HERE ON OFFICIAL BUSINESS

I'M THE CHAPERONE
THE WHAT?
JIM DAVIS 9-11
© 1992 United Feature Syndicate, Inc.

HEY! HEY! CUT THAT OUT, YOU TWO!
MRS. FRONZAK, THEY'RE MARRIED

WATCH THIS, GARFIELD! I'LL SHOW MY OLD CLASSMATES I STILL HAVE ALL THE MOVES!
9-12

BOOGIE! BOOGIE! BOOGIE!
JIM DAVIS
© 1992 United Feature Syndicate, Inc.

LET'S BOOGIE ON HOME. I'LL LEAD

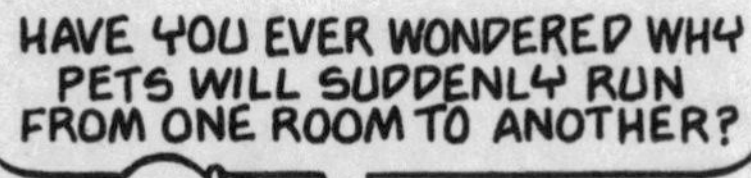

© 1992 United Feature Syndicate, Inc.

© 1992 United Feature Syndicate, Inc.

© 1992 United Feature Syndicate, Inc.

© 1992 United Feature Syndicate, Inc.

© 1992 United Feature Syndicate, Inc.

© 1992 United Feature Syndicate, Inc.

© 1992 United Feature Syndicate, Inc.

© 1992 United Feature Syndicate, Inc.

© 1992 United Feature Syndicate, Inc.

© 1992 United Feature Syndicate, Inc.

© 1992 United Feature Syndicate, Inc.

© 1992 United Feature Syndicate, Inc.

© 1992 United Feature Syndicate, Inc.

© 1992 United Feature Syndicate, Inc.

DRILL
DRILL
DRILL
DRILL
© 1992 United Feature Syndicate, Inc.

JIM DAVIS 9-30

SNIFFFFFF

GOOSH!!

© 1992 United Feature Syndicate, Inc.

© 1992 United Feature Syndicate, Inc.

I SEE YOU'RE READY TO POUNCE, GARFIELD

YOU BET!
© 1992 United Feature Syndicate, Inc.

THEY'RE BAKING A CAKE!
JIM DAVIS 10-3

© 1992 United Feature Syndicate, Inc.

© 1992 United Feature Syndicate, Inc.

© 1992 United Feature Syndicate, Inc.
JIM DAVIS 10-7

THAT'S THE BIGGEST SLINGSHOT I'VE EVER SEEN

CHEER UP, GARFIELD! LET A SMILE BE YOUR UMBRELLA!

THAT'S WHAT MY AUNT EDNA USED TO SAY
© 1992 United Feature Syndicate, Inc.

TILL A BOLT OF LIGHTNING BLEW HER DENTURES CLEAN THROUGH THE GARAGE DOOR

A BEAUTIFUL EVENING, GARFIELD

FULL MOON... WARM BREEZE...
JIM DAVIS 10-9
© 1992 United Feature Syndicate, Inc.

THE NEIGHBORS TAKING SLEDGEHAMMERS TO THE LAWN ORNAMENTS
GET AWAY FROM THERE!

© 1992 United Feature Syndicate, Inc.

© 1992 United Feature Syndicate, Inc.

OKAY, MOUSE... THIS IS IT!
JIM DAVIS 10-13

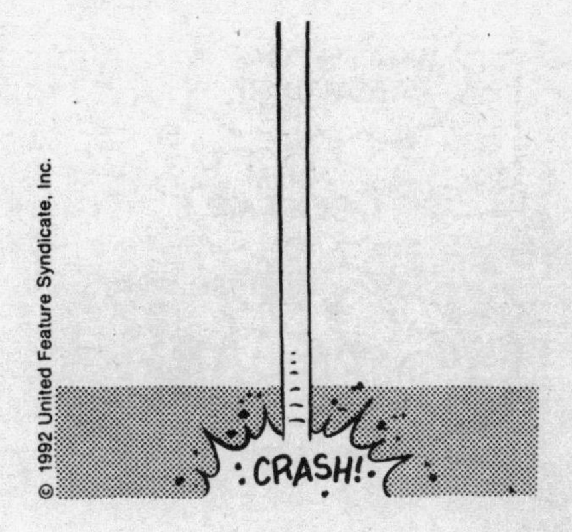
CRASH!
© 1992 United Feature Syndicate, Inc.

© 1992 United Feature Syndicate, Inc.

© 1992 United Feature Syndicate, Inc.

DUPLEX
JIM DAVIS 10-15

© 1992 United Feature Syndicate, Inc.

© 1992 United Feature Syndicate, Inc.

© 1992 United Feature Syndicate, Inc.

DINNER!

GARY

© 1992 United Feature Syndicate, Inc
JIM DAVIS 10-20

THIS LOOKS LIKE A GOOD PLACE TO MAKE CAMP
© 1992 United Feature Syndicate, Inc.

JIM DAVIS 10·21
MUNCH
MUNCH
MUNCH
MUNCH

© 1992 United Feature Syndicate, Inc.

© 1992 United Feature Syndicate, Inc.

© 1992 United Feature Syndicate, Inc.

© 1992 United Feature Syndicate, Inc.

© 1992 United Feature Syndicate, Inc.

© 1992 United Feature Syndicate, Inc.

BOO!

NICE TRY, GARFIELD. BUT YOU'RE NOT GETTING MY FOOD
© 1992 United Feature Syndicate, Inc.

JIM DAVIS 10-29

© 1992 United Feature Syndicate, Inc.

© 1992 United Feature Syndicate, Inc.

© 1992 United Feature Syndicate, Inc.

© 1992 United Feature Syndicate, Inc.

© 1992 United Feature Syndicate, Inc.

© 1992 United Feature Syndicate, Inc.

© 1992 United Feature Syndicate, Inc.

© 1992 United Feature Syndicate, Inc.

© 1992 United Feature Syndicate, Inc.

© 1992 United Feature Syndicate, Inc.

© 1992 United Feature Syndicate, Inc.

© 1992 United Feature Syndicate, Inc.

© 1992 United Feature Syndicate, Inc JIM DAVIS 11-13

© 1992 United Feature Syndicate, Inc.

Y'KNOW, GARFIELD, THE MORE ZIPPERS A MAN HAS, THE MORE MACHO HE IS!

TAKE A GANDER AT THIS OUTFIT. IT HAS SIX GAJILLION ZIPPERS!
JPM DAVIS 11-16
© 1992 United Feature Syndicate, Inc.

NOW WHERE DID I PUT MY KEYS?
PAT PAT
PAT PAT
THIS COULD TAKE MONTHS!

© 1992 United Feature Syndicate, Inc.

© 1992 United Feature Syndicate, Inc.

© 1992 United Feature Syndicate, Inc.

© 1992 United Feature Syndicate, Inc.

I WONDER IF GARFIELD KNOWS I HAVE A PIZZA IN THE OVEN

© 1992 United Feature Syndicate, Inc.
JIM DAVIS 11-21

I WONDER IF JON KNOWS I ATE HIS PIZZA
HE DOESN'T SUSPECT A THING

© 1992 United Feature Syndicate, Inc.

YEEHAAAA!
I HATE THE BEACH

SPLOOSH!
© 1992 United Feature Syndicate, Inc.
JIM DAVIS 11-24

EEEEK!
BUT, IT DOES HAVE ITS MOMENTS

© 1992 United Feature Syndicate, Inc.

© 1992 United Feature Syndicate, Inc.

DO YOU THINK I'M GETTING A SUNBURN, GARFIELD?
ONLY ONE WAY TO TELL

SLAP!
© 1992 United Feature Syndicate, Inc.
JIM DAVIS 11-27

YEEEOOOOW!
YOU'RE GETTING A SUNBURN

© 1992 United Feature Syndicate, Inc.

© 1992 United Feature Syndicate, Inc.

© 1992 United Feature Syndicate, Inc.

BEWARE
OF
DOG

BEWARE
OF
DOG
© 1992 United Feature Syndicate, Inc.

JIM DAVIS 12-2

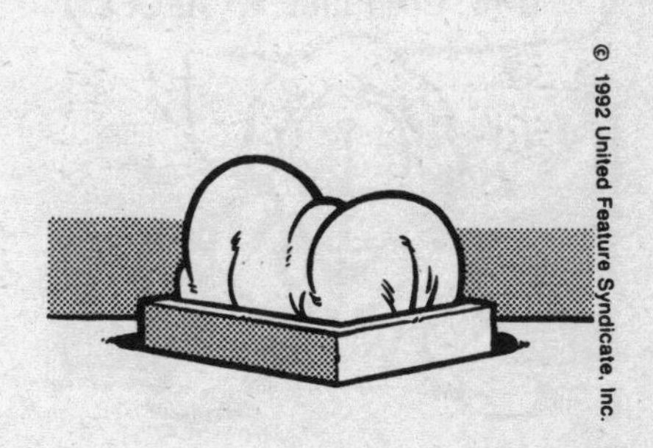

© 1992 United Feature Syndicate, Inc.

© 1992 United Feature Syndicate, Inc.

© 1992 United Feature Syndicate, Inc.
JIM DAVIS 12-5

I'M GETTING ORGANIZED
TO EAT
EATEN

© 1992 United Feature Syndicate, Inc.

© 1992 United Feature Syndicate, Inc.

© 1992 United Feature Syndicate, Inc.

© 1992 United Feature Syndicate, Inc.

YOU ARE LAZY, GARFIELD, AND YOU CAN'T DENY IT!

I CAN SO DENY IT!
© 1992 United Feature Syndicate, Inc.

I JUST DON'T FEEL LIKE IT, THAT'S ALL
JIM DAVIS 12-11

© 1992 United Feature Syndicate, Inc.

© 1992 United Feature Syndicate, Inc.

CHRISTMAS
IS COMING
JIM DAVIS 12-14

WE'RE LOOKING FOR A CHRISTMAS TREE
HOW ABOUT AN ARTIFICIAL ONE?
TREES

WHAT'S THE DIFFERENCE?
YOU DON'T HAVE TO WATER AN ARTIFICIAL TREE
TREES
© 1992 United Feature Syndicate, Inc.

JIM DAVIS
SO?
WE DON'T WATER THE REAL ONES ANYWAY

© 1992 United Feature Syndicate, Inc.

♪
AH, THE TRADITIONAL "BRINGING THE CHRISTMAS DECORATIONS DOWN FROM THE ATTIC"

♪
JPM DAVIS 12-17
© 1992 United Feature Syndicate, Inc.

ALONG WITH THE ALSO-TRADITIONAL "FINDING OF THE BIG, HAIRY SPIDER IN THE BOX"

JOIN US NOW, WON'T YOU?
JIM DAVIS 12-18

IN OUR TRADITIONAL HOLIDAY SEARCH...
© 1992 United Feature Syndicate, Inc.

FOR THE ONE BAD BULB IN A STRING OF FIVE ZILLION THAT MAKES THE OTHERS GO OUT

© 1992 United Feature Syndicate, Inc.

© 1992 United Feature Syndicate, Inc.

WHAT COULD BE MORE TRADITIONAL THAN THE HANGING OF A CHRISTMAS WREATH ON THE DOOR?

© 1992 United Feature Syndicate, Inc.
JIM DAVIS 12-22

© 1992 United Feature Syndicate, Inc.

NO WAY I'M GONNA MISS SEEING SANTA THIS YEAR!

IF I HAVE TO, I'LL STAY... AWAKE... ALL...
© 1992 United Feature Syndicate, Inc.

Z
JIM DAVIS 12-24

© 1992 United Feature Syndicate, Inc.

© 1992 United Feature Syndicate, Inc.

© 1992 United Feature Syndicate, Inc.

TONIGHT I'LL BE MIMING THE NEWS!

© 1992 United Feature Syndicate, Inc.

WHAT THE?...
EITHER ALIENS HAVE LANDED OR THE AARDVARK'S PANTS ARE TOO SHORT
JIM DAVIS 12-29

© 1992 United Feature Syndicate, Inc.

Garfield

In Training

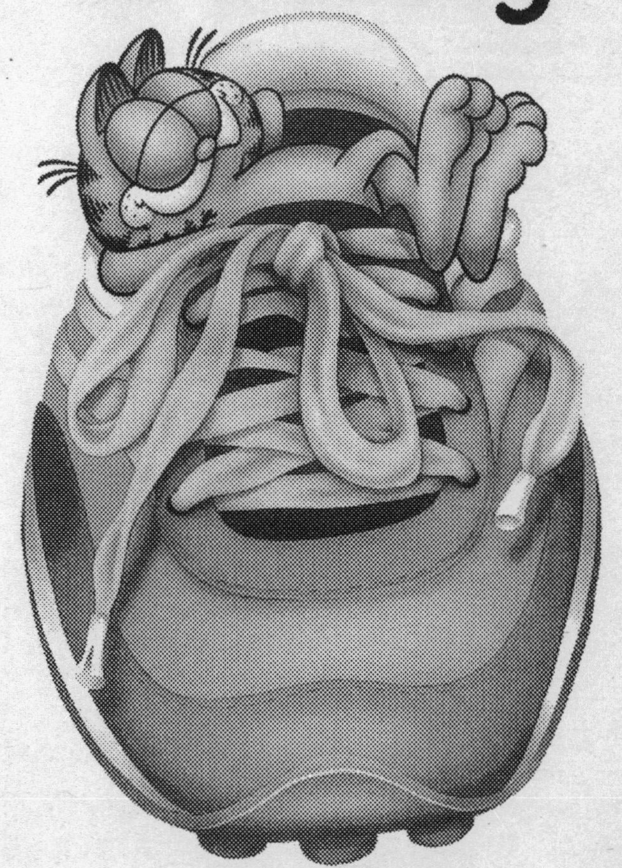

JIM DAVIS

RR

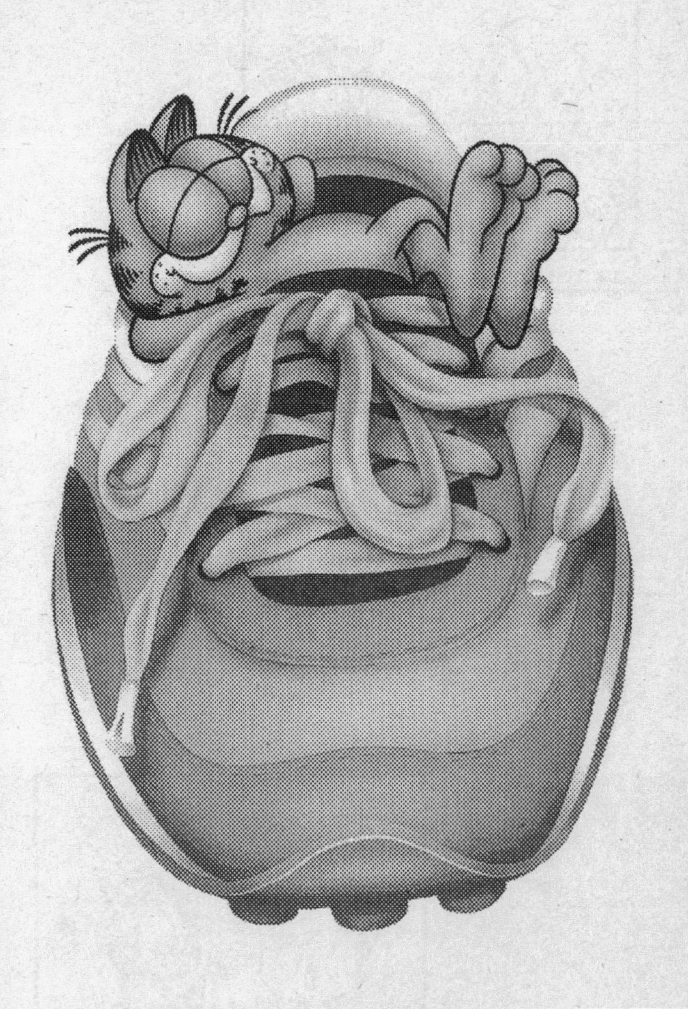

© 1992 United Feature Syndicate, Inc

© 1992 United Feature Syndicate, Inc

© 1992 United Feature Syndicate, Inc.

© 1992 United Feature Syndicate, Inc.

© 1992 United Feature Syndicate, Inc.

© 1992 United Feature Syndicate, Inc.

© 1992 United Feature Syndicate, Inc.

THIS IS THE NATIONAL CAT NETWORK

NOW BACK TO OUR FEATURE PRESENTATION...
© 1992 United Feature Syndicate, Inc.

"LASSIE CROSSES THE FREEWAY"
I'M ROOTING FOR THE TRUCKS
JIM DAVIS 1-8-93

© 1992 United Feature Syndicate, Inc.

GARFIELD, WHAT DO YOU THINK OF OUR REFRIGERATOR?
IT KEEPS THE FOOD OFF THE FLOOR

DO YOU THINK WE SHOULD GET A NEW ONE?
DO YOU THINK AIR WILL CATCH ON AS A BREATHING MEDIUM?
© 1993 United Feature Syndicate, Inc.
JIM DAVIS 1-11

WHAT SAY WE GO SHOPPING?
JON, YOU DON'T "SHOP" FOR A REFRIGERATOR, YOU MAKE A COMMITMENT

© 1993 United Feature Syndicate, Inc.

© 1993 United Feature Syndicate, Inc.

© 1993 United Feature Syndicate, Inc.

FOR THE DIETER, HERE'S A FRIDGE WITH A FULL-LENGTH MIRROR
ABSURD
JIM DAVIS

FOR THE INDECISIVE DINER, THIS ONE FEATURES A PEEPHOLE
SILLY
1-15
© 1993 United Feature Syndicate, Inc.

AND FOR THE CAT OWNER... A PET DOOR
PRACTICAL

NOW THIS FRIDGE HAS A 19" TV INSTALLED RIGHT IN THE DOOR

AND FOR THE HOPELESSLY DECADENT...
JIM DAVIS 1-16
© 1993 United Feature Syndicate, Inc.

A ROLL AWAY BED!
WHAT? NO HOT TUB?

© 1993 United Feature Syndicate, Inc.

© 1993 United Feature Syndicate, Inc.

© 1993 United Feature Syndicate, Inc.

© 1993 United Feature Syndicate, Inc

© 1993 United Feature Syndicate, Inc.

© 1993 United Feature Syndicate, Inc.

© 1993 United Feature Syndicate, Inc.

EVER WAKE UP FEELING DEPRESSED, GARFIELD?
JIM DAVIS 1-26

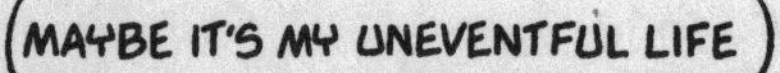
MAYBE IT'S MY UNEVENTFUL LIFE

© 1993 United Feature Syndicate, Inc.

OR MAYBE IT'S BECAUSE YOU GLUED MY HAND TO MY FACE!!
SURE, BLAME ME

© 1993 United Feature Syndicate, Inc.

JIM DAVIS 1-28

LET'S DO SOMETHING
I THOUGHT WE WERE
© 1993 United Feature Syndicate, Inc.

SOMETHING WHERE WE MOVE
YOU LOST ME

© 1993 United Feature Syndicate, Inc.

© 1993 United Feature Syndicate, Inc.

© 1993 United Feature Syndicate, Inc.

YOU GET THE HOUSE FILTHY, AND I CLEAN IT!
JIM DAVIS 2-2

YOU GET THE HOUSE FILTHY, AND I CLEAN IT!
© 1993 United Feature Syndicate, Inc.

AH, THE DELICATE BALANCE OF NATURE

© 1993 United Feature Syndicate, Inc.

© 1993 United Feature Syndicate, Inc.

© 1993 United Feature Syndicate, Inc.

© 1993 United Feature Syndicate, Inc.

© 1993 United Feature Syndicate, Inc.

© 1993 United Feature Syndicate, Inc.

© 1993 United Feature Syndicate, Inc.

LET GO, GARFIELD! I HAVE A NET!

© 1993 United Feature Syndicate, Inc.
BOING!

JIM DAVIS 2-11

© 1993 United Feature Syndicate, Inc.

© 1993 United Feature Syndicate, Inc.

© 1993 United Feature Syndicate, Inc.

© 1993 United Feature Syndicate, Inc.

© 1993 United Feature Syndicate, Inc.

© 1993 United Feature Syndicate, Inc.

© 1993 United Feature Syndicate, Inc.

© 1993 United Feature Syndicate, Inc.

© 1993 United Feature Syndicate, Inc.

© 1993 United Feature Syndicate, Inc.

ARLENE, DO YOU MIND IF I DO SOMETHING IMPETUOUS?
GO AHEAD

BARK! BARK! BARK!
JIM DAVIS 2-24
© 1993 United Feature Syndicate, Inc.

YOUR KEY OR MINE, ARLENE?

MINE
OF COURSE, MY DEAR
JIM DAVIS 2-25
© 1993 United Feature Syndicate, Inc.

ROWRRRRR

WHO'S THAT?
THAT'S ODIE, ARLENE

BOOT!
JIM DAVIS 2-26
© 1993 United Feature Syndicate, Inc.

HE KICKS REAL NICE
DOESN'T HE THOUGH?

IT'S BEEN A PERFECT EVENING
YES, IT HAS

GOOD NIGHT, ARLENE
GOOD NIGHT, GARFIELD
JIM DAVIS 2-27
© 1993 United Feature Syndicate, Inc.

SMACK

BOY, THE DAYS FLY BY FAST...
SEEMS EVERY TIME
YOU TURN AROUND...

SPLUT!
© 1993 United Feature Syndicate, Inc.
JIM DAVIS 3-1

IT'S
MONDAY
AGAIN

© 1993 United Feature Syndicate, Inc.

© 1993 United Feature Syndicate, Inc.

TWO ASTRONAUTS HOVERING ABOVE A HOSTILE PLANET

BOOT!
© 1993 United Feature Syndicate, Inc.

ONE OPTS TO STAY ABOARD WHILE THE OTHER BEAMS DOWN TO THE SURFACE
JIM DAVIS 3-4

© 1993 United Feature Syndicate, Inc

JON GAVE ME THIS TURTLE TO KEEP ME AMUSED

I'M TAKING IT FOR A WALK
© 1993 United Feature Syndicate, Inc.

WOAH! SLOW DOWN, BOY!
JIM DAVIS 3-6

© 1993 United Feature Syndicate, Inc.

© 1993 United Feature Syndicate, Inc.

© 1993 United Feature Syndicate, Inc.

© 1993 United Feature Syndicate, Inc.

© 1993 United Feature Syndicate, Inc.

© 1993 United Feature Syndicate, Inc.

FETCH, ODIE!

© 1993 United Feature Syndicate, Inc.

THAT SHOULD KEEP HIM BUSY THE REST OF THE WEEK
JIM DAVIS 3-15

© 1993 United Feature Syndicate, Inc.

© 1993 United Feature Syndicate, Inc.

THIS IS MY UNCLE, "TOUGH BOB"
ALBUM

HE ONCE HAD SURGERY WITH NO ANESTHETIC!
THAT IS TOUGH!
© 1993 United Feature Syndicate, Inc.

SOON AFTER, THEY CHANGED HIS NAME TO "SCREAMING BOB"
HE SURE HAS BIG EYES
ALBU
JIM DAVIS 3-18

© 1993 United Feature Syndicate, Inc.

© 1993 United Feature Syndicate, Inc.

© 1993 United Feature Syndicate, Inc.

© 1993 United Feature Syndicate, Inc.

© 1993 United Feature Syndicate, Inc.

© 1993 United Feature Syndicate, Inc.

I LIKE TO EAT FROM EACH OF THE THREE BASIC FOOD GROUPS: WHAT'S IN MY BOWL...
GARFIELD

WHAT'S ON JON'S PLATE...
ELD
© 1993 United Feature Syndicate, Inc.

AND WHAT'S LEFT OVER
GARFIELD!
JIM DAVIS 3-26

© 1993 United Feature Syndicate, Inc.

TA-DAH!
© 1983 United Feature Syndicate, Inc.

YOU LIKE YOURSELF, DON'T YOU?
WHO WOULDN'T?
JIM DAVIS 3-29

© 1993 United Feature Syndicate, Inc.

© 1993 United Feature Syndicate, Inc.

© 1993 United Feature Syndicate, Inc.

© 1993 United Feature Syndicate, Inc.

© 1993 United Feature Syndicate, Inc.

GARFIELD, FOR EVERY MAN, THERE'S A WOMAN
SPARE ME

MINE IS OUT THERE SOMEWHERE
PROBABLY IN HIDING
© 1993 United Feature Syndicate, Inc.

I JUST GOTTA KEEP LOOKING
I'LL CHECK UNDER A ROCK
JIM DAVIS 4-5

HI, THIS IS SUZY. I'M NOT AT HOME, BUT PLEASE LEAVE A MESSAGE AT THE TONE...

UNLESS YOU'RE JON ARBUCKLE, IN WHICH CASE THE MACHINE WILL AUTOMATICALLY HANG UP.
...BEEP!
© 1993 United Feature Syndicate, Inc.

THIS IS, UH, ED SMITH
CLICK-BZZZZZZ
JUST AMAZING

AFTER DINNER WE CAN COME BACK TO MY PLACE, MY DEAR...

THEN WE CAN PUT ON GRASS SKIRTS AND CARVE MONKEY HEADS IN COCONUTS
JIM DAVIS 4-7
© 1993 United Feature Syndicate, Inc.

CLICK!
HELLO?
HENCE THE MONIKER, "MR. DIAL TONE"

© 1993 United Feature Syndicate, Inc.

LET'S DRINK OUT OF EACH OTHER'S GLASSES

HOW ROMANTIC!
© 1993 United Feature Syndicate, Inc.

ACTUALLY, MY LAST DATE TRIED TO POISON ME

© 1993 United Feature Syndicate, Inc.

© 1993 United Feature Syndicate, Inc.

© 1993 United Feature Syndicate, Inc.

YOU CAN'T HAVE THIS CHAIR, GARFIELD. I'M NOT MOVING... NO MATTER WHAT!

GREAT!
JIM DAVIS 4-14
© 1993 United Feature Syndicate, Inc.

WHAT ARE YOU UP TO?!

© 1993 United Feature Syndicate, Inc.

© 1993 United Feature Syndicate, Inc.

GREETINGS, EARTHLING

I COME TO YOUR PLANET IN PEACE
© 1993 United Feature Syndicate, Inc.

TAKE ME TO YOUR COOK
JIM DAVIS 4-17

© 1993 United Feature Syndicate, Inc.

© 1993 United Feature Syndicate, Inc.

© 1993 United Feature Syndicate, Inc.

THIS RESTAURANT IS SO FANCY, WHEN YOU ORDER MILK, THEY BRING THE COW TO YOUR TABLE!

SQUIIRT!
4-22
© 1993 United Feature Syndicate, Inc.

NO OFFENSE, MA'AM
MOO
JIM DAVIS

WHAT DO YOU GET IF YOU REMOVE HALF A CAT'S BRAIN?

YOU GET A SMART DOG!
© 1993 United Feature Syndicate, Inc.
JIM DAVIS
4-23

THANK YOU! PLEASE HOLD YOUR ADULATION TILL THE END OF THE PERFORMANCE!

BOO!
WELL, YOU'VE BEEN A LOVELY AUDIENCE

BOO!
I'D LIKE TO GIVE YOU ALL A BIG HUG AND A KISS
JPM DAVPS 4.24
© 1993 United Feature Syndicate, Inc.

BOO!
HOW ABOUT A GOOD SLAP AND A LIVE BADGER UP THE NOSE?

© 1993 United Feature Syndicate, Inc.

© 1993 United Feature Syndicate, Inc.

AND NOW IT'S TIME FOR...

BOWLING FOR BEAN DIP!
© 1993 United Feature Syndicate, Inc.
JIM DAVIS 4-28

BROUGHT TO YOU BY...
GARFIELD, WHEREVER YOU ARE, LEAVE THE REMOTE CONTROL ALONE!

© 1993 United Feature Syndicate, Inc.

© 1993 United Feature Syndicate, Inc.

© 1993 United Feature Syndicate, Inc.

© 1993 United Feature Syndicate, Inc.

© 1993 United Feature Syndicate, Inc.

© 1993 United Feature Syndicate, Inc.

© 1993 United Feature Syndicate, Inc.

© 1993 United Feature Syndicate, Inc.

© 1993 United Feature Syndicate, Inc.

CAT HAIR!

CAT HAIR FOR EVERYONE!
© 1993 United Feature Syndicate, Inc.

I HATE SHEDDING SEASON
JIM DAVIS 5-10

JIM DAVIS 5-11
YOU'RE SHEDDING

© 1993 United Feature Syndicate, Inc.

I PREFER TO THINK OF IT AS LOSING WEIGHT

© 1993 United Feature Syndicate, Inc.

SHED
SHED
SHED
SHED
SHED
SHED

SHED
SHED
SHED
SHED
SHED
SHED
SHED
SHED
SHED
SHED
© 1993 United Feature Syndicate, Inc.

HOW ABOUT CALLING IT A DRAW?
URF
JPM DAVPS 5-13

CAT HAIR!

WHY IS EVERYTHING I OWN COVERED WITH CAT HAIR?!
© 1993 United Feature Syndicate, Inc.

I NEED BROWN SOCKS
JIM DAVIS 5-14

© 1993 United Feature Syndicate, Inc.

© 1993 United Feature Syndicate, Inc.

© 1993 United Feature Syndicate, Inc.

© 1993 United Feature Syndicate, Inc.

© 1993 United Feature Syndicate, Inc.

© 1993 United Feature Syndicate, Inc.

HERE WE ARE AT THE AMUSEMENT PARK
JIM DAVIS 5-22
PHOTO ALBUM

THOSE RIDES WERE SURE SCARY
WE GOT THROWN OUT
© 1993 United Feature Syndicate, Inc.

I COULDN'T STOP SCREAMING
HE SPOOKED THE PONIES

OTHER GARFIELD BOOKS AVAILABLE

Pocket Books	Price	ISBN
Bon Appetit	£3.50	1 84161 038 0
Byte Me	£3.50	1 84161 009 7
Double Trouble	£3.50	1 84161 008 9
Eat My Dust	£3.50	1 84161 098 4
Fun in the Sun	£3.50	1 84161 097 6
The Gladiator	£3.50	1 85304 941 7
Gooooooal!	£3.50	1 84161 037 2
Great Impressions	£3.50	1 85304 191 2
Hangs On	£2.99	1 85304 784 8
In Training	£3.50	1 85304 785 6
The Irresistible	£3.50	1 85304 940 9
Let's Party	£3.50	1 85304 906 9
Light Of My Life	£3.50	1 85304 353 2
On The Right Track	£3.50	1 85304 907 7
Pick Of The Bunch	£2.99	1 85304 258 7
Says It With Flowers	£2.99	1 85304 316 8
Shove At First Sight	£3.50	1 85304 990 5
To Eat, Or Not To Eat?	£3.50	1 85304 991 3
Wave Rebel	£3.50	1 85304 317 6
With Love From Me To You	£3.50	1 85304 392 3
new titles available February 2003		
No. 45 – Pop Star	£3.50	1 84161 151 4
No. 46 – Below Par	£3.50	1 84161 152 2
Theme Books		
Guide to Behaving Badly	£4.50	1 85304 892 5
Guide to Cat Napping	£4.50	1 84161 087 9
Guide to Coffee Mornings	£4.50	1 84161 086 0
Guide to Creatures Great & Small	£3.99	1 85304 998 0
Guide to Healthy Living	£3.99	1 85304 972 7
Guide to Insults	£3.99	1 85304 895 X
Guide to Pigging Out	£4.50	1 85304 893 3
Guide to Romance	£3.99	1 85304 894 1
Guide to The Seasons	£3.99	1 85304 999 9
Guide to Successful Living	£3.99	1 85304 973 5
new series now available		
2-in-1 Theme Books		
The Gruesome Twosome	£6.99	1 84161 143 3
Out For The Couch	£6.99	1 84161 144 1

Classics	Price	ISBN
Volume One	£5.99	1 85304 970 0
Volume Two	£5.99	1 85304 971 9
Volume Three	£5.99	1 85304 996 4
Volume Four	£5.99	1 85304 997 2
Volume Five	£5.99	1 84161 022 4
Volume Six	£5.99	1 84161 023 2
Volume Seven	£5.99	1 84161 088 7
Volume Eight	£5.99	1 84161 089 5
new title now available		
Volume Nine	£5.99	1 84161 149 2
new series now available		
Little Books		
Food 'n' Fitness	£2.50	1 84161 145 X
Laughs	£2.50	1 84161 146 8
Love 'n' Stuff	£2.50	1 84161 147 6
Wit 'n' Wisdom	£2.50	1 84161 148 4
Miscellaneous		
new title available September 2002		
Treasury 3	£9.99	1 84161 142 5
Treasury 2	£9.99	1 84161 042 9
Address Book (indexed)	inc vat £4.99	1 85304 904 2
21st Birthday Celebration Book	£9.99	1 85304 995 6

All Garfield books are available at your local bookshop or from the publisher at the address below. Just tick the titles required and send the form with your payment to:-

RAVETTE PUBLISHING
Unit 3, Tristar Centre, Star Road, Partridge Green, West Sussex RH13 8RA

Prices and availability are subject to change without notice.
Please enclose a cheque or postal order made payable to **Ravette Publishing** to the value of the cover price of the book and allow the following for UK postage and packing:

60p for the first book + 30p for each additional book
except *Garfield Treasuries* and *21st Birthday Celebration Book* . . . when please add £3.00 per copy for p&p

Name ....

Address ....

....

....